FUN AND GAMES
with the
RECORDER

TUNE **1** BOOK

Method for descant recorder

Gerhard Engel · Gudrun Heyens

Konrad Hünteler · Hans-Martin Linde

Translated and adapted by Peter Bowman

With illustrations
by Julie Beech and John Minnion

SCHOTT
EDUCATIONAL
PUBLICATIONS

Contents

About the tunes

Tunes **1** to **8** use the notes **B**, **A** and **G**.

Tunes **9** to **11** use the new notes **E** and **C**.

Tunes **12** to **26** use the full range of notes learned in **Tutor Book 1**.

Although sharp signs appear in many pieces as a key signature, no notes beyond those learned in **Tutor Book 1** are played. The student's knowledge of notation is expanded by the use of semibreve notes and rests from the very first tune.

Please note that, whilst the first recorder part is always playable by the student, the second (and third) recorder parts are sometimes more difficult. In tunes **14**, **15** and **26** the parts are equal. Students who have completed **Tutor Book 2** will be able to play the second part in tunes **5** and **20** whilst a student will need to have completed **Tutor Book 3** to play tunes **7** (both second and third parts), **18** and **21**.

The pieces use conventional bar numbering starting with 1 for the first full bar.

 This symbol is used to indicate a piece which has a *piano* accompaniment in the **Insert**. The music in the piano part may be written using repeat bars but the student's music is always written out in full to avoid unnecessary explanation.

 This symbol is used on those pieces which use *guitar chords* to provide an accompaniment.

ED 12591

British Library Cataloguing-in-Publication Data.
A catalogue record for this book is available from the British Library.

ISMN M-2201-1910-1

Cover, pages 1 and 20 illustrations Julie Beech
All other illustrations John Minnion
Design The Design Works, Reading
Music setting Halstan & Co.

1 Children's dance

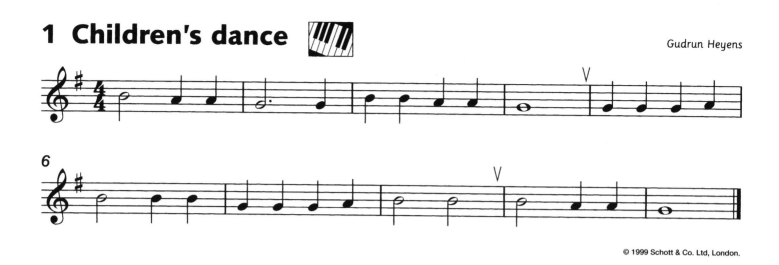

Gudrun Heyens

2 Suo gân

Traditional Welsh

Lul - la - by, lul - la - by, sleep my babe, do not cry.

Lul - la - by, lul - la - by, sleep my babe, do not cry.

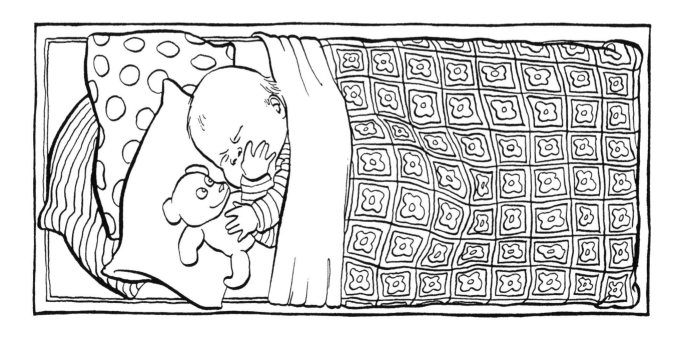

3 Farmer's song

Philip Rodgers

From: *20 Simple Tunes*, Schott ED 10273

4 Fairy song

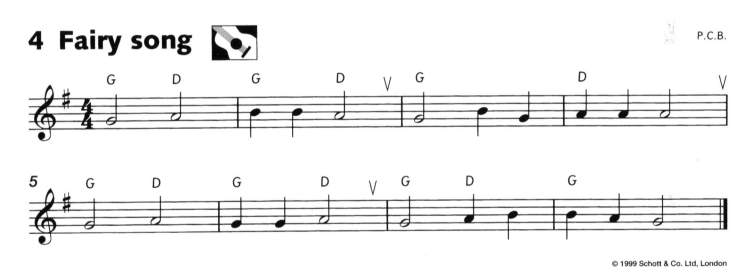

P.C.B.

5 Little duet

Gudrun Heyens

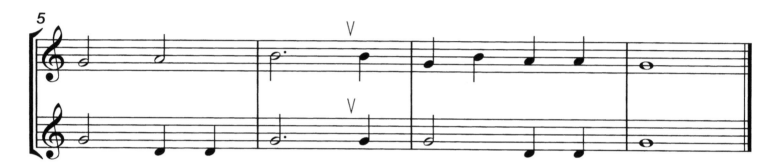

6 Little dance

P.C.B.

7 Dance

Gudrun Heyens

8 Au clair de la lune

French folksong

** In the middle section the piano takes over the melody.
Count to 4 four times and find your entry yourself.*

9 Russian melody

Gudrun Heyens

10 From China

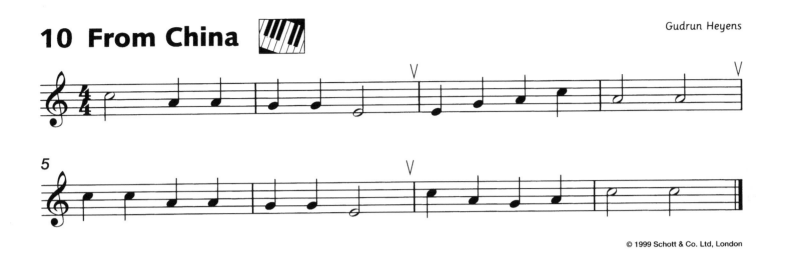

Gudrun Heyens

11 Evening song

Philip Rodgers

12 Sad song

Nursery rhyme

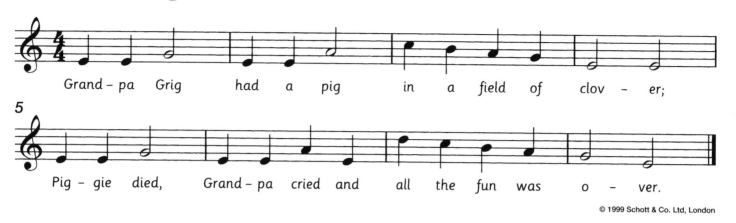

Grand - pa Grig had a pig in a field of clov - er;

Pig - gie died, Grand - pa cried and all the fun was o - ver.

13 The students are happy

Traditional English

14 Three farmers

Forster, 1540
Setting: Willi Drahts

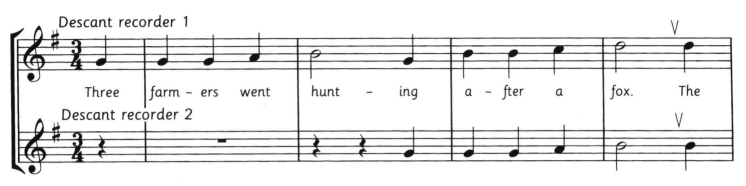

15 Chasings

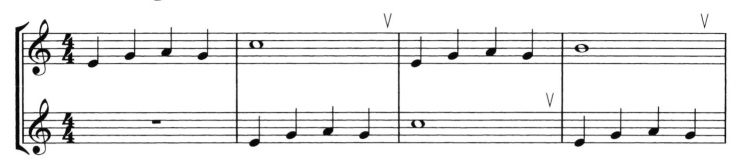

16 Rigadoon

Henry Purcell

17 Aunt Nancy

Nursery rhyme

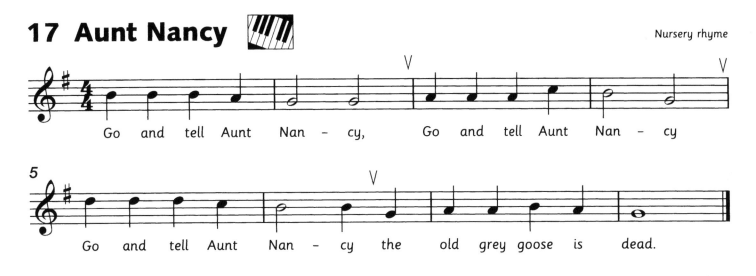

Go and tell Aunt Nan - cy, Go and tell Aunt Nan - cy

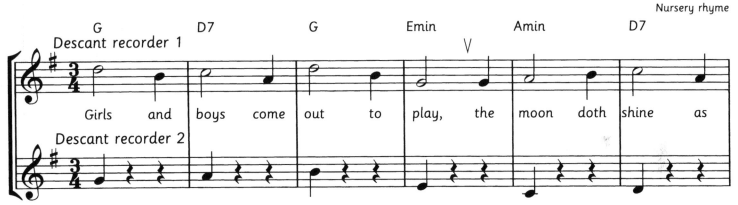

Go and tell Aunt Nan - cy the old grey goose is dead.

From: *20 Simple Tunes*, ED 10273

18 Girls and boys come out to play

Nursery rhyme

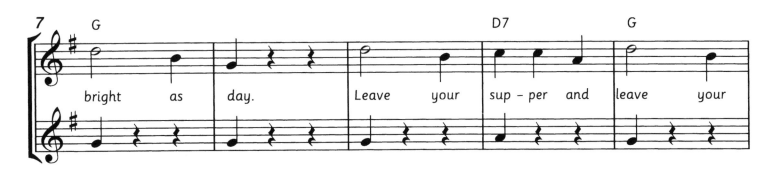

Descant recorder 1

Girls and boys come out to play, the moon doth shine as

Descant recorder 2

bright as day. Leave your sup - per and leave your

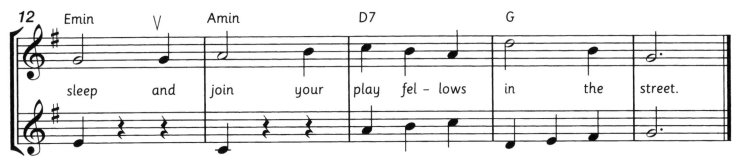

sleep and join your play fel - lows in the street.

19 Little bird

Children's song

20 Hänsel and Gretel

Setting: Hans-Martin Linde

21 Little Bo-Peep

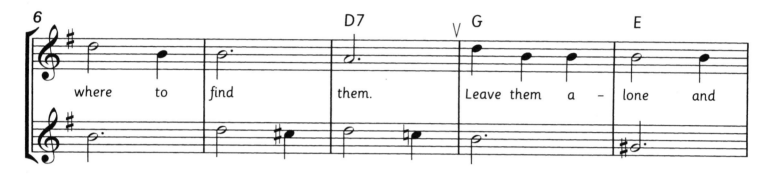

Descant recorder 1

G   Amin   D   G

Lit – tle Bo – Peep has lost her sheep and does – n't know

Descant recorder 2

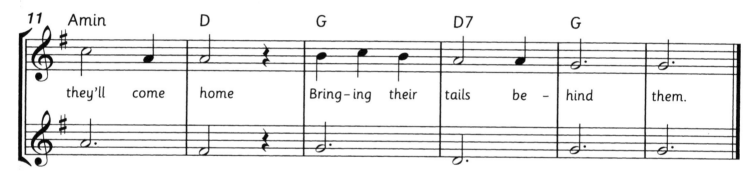

6

D7   G   E

where to find them. Leave them a – lone and

11   Amin   D   G   D7   G

they'll come home Bring–ing their tails be – hind them.

© 1999 Schott & Co. Ltd, London

22 In Summer

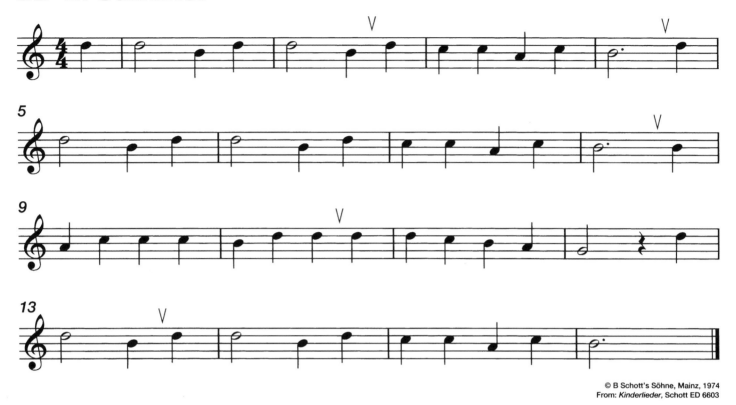

23 The bear

P.C.B.

Look at the bear climb-ing the tree, I hope he'll stay there it's saf - er for me. He's get - ting cross, Now I must run, run - ning a - way from a bear's not much fun.

24 Swedish children's song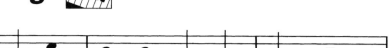

25 Spring-time dance

Traditional Swiss

26 Alarm using 5 notes

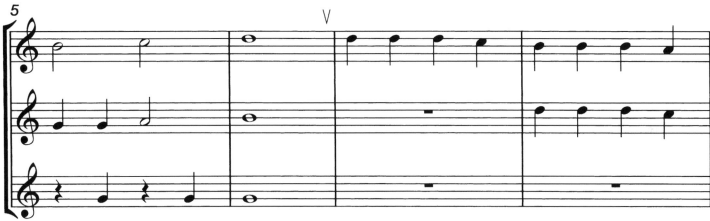

From: F.J. Giesbert, *Schule des Zusammenspiels für 3 Sopranblockflöten,* Schott ED 5585

Index of tunes

Goodbye everyone!
I hope you've had lots of fun.
I look forward to seeing you
again in **Tune Book 2** of
**Fun and Games with
the Recorder**.

FUN AND GAMES
with the
RECORDER

TUNE **1** BOOK

PIANO ACCOMPANIMENT
INSERT

Method for descant recorder

ED 12591-01

SCHOTT
EDUCATIONAL
PUBLICATIONS

Contents

ED 12591-01

British Library Cataloguing-in-Publication Data.
A catalogue record for this book is available from the
British Library.

ISMN M-2201-1936-1

© 1999 Schott & Co. Ltd, London

Illustrations Julie Beech

1 Children's dance

Gudrun Heyens

3 Farmer's song

Philip Rodgers

8 Au clair de la lune

French folksong
Setting: Hans-Martin Linde

9 Russian melody

Gudrun Heyens
Setting: Hans-Martin Linde

10 From China

Gudrun Heyens
Setting: Hans-Martin Linde

7

11 Evening song

Philip Rodgers

From: *20 Simple Tunes*, ED 10273

8

13 The students are happy

Traditional English
Setting: Hans-Martin Linde

16 Rigadoon

Henry Purcell

17 Aunt Nancy

Nursery rhyme

Go and tell Aunt Nan – cy, Go and tell Aunt Nan – cy

Go and tell Aunt Nan – cy the old grey goose is dead.

From: *20 Simple Tunes*, ED 10273

24 Swedish children's song

Setting: Fritz Emonts

12